Major Scales in similar motion
Hands separately and together an octave apart: 2 octaves: ♩ = 80

28.06, 13.07,

Minor Scales (melodic *or* harmonic at candidate's choice) in similar motion
Hands separately and together an octave apart: 2 octaves: ♩ = 80

Scales, Arpeggios & Broken Chords

Piano

Grade 3

Good legato, even fingers, firm tone and a musical curve are the essential features for playing scales and arpeggios well.

The suggested fingering shown here is not obligatory; any practical and systematic fingering which produces a good result will be accepted in the examination. Some alternative fingering is shown as follows: **4/3**. In the playing of arpeggios, the decision as to which fingering to adopt will depend on the size and shape of the player's hand. Examiners do not comment on the choice of fingering unless it interferes with an even, legato flow.

In the examination, all scales, arpeggios and broken chords must be played from memory.

Metronome marks shown here indicate *minimum* recommended speeds for the examination.

Reference must always be made to the syllabus for the year in which the examination is to be taken, in case any changes have been made to the requirements.

The Associated Board of the Royal Schools of Music

Major Scales in contrary motion
Hands together beginning and ending on the key-note (unison): 2 octaves: ♩ = 80

Chromatic Scales
Hands separately: 2 octaves (only 1 octave is shown below): ♩ = 80

5

Arpeggios of major and minor common chords in root position

Hands separately: 2 octaves: ♩ = 69

Broken Chords

Hands separately: Pattern 1 *or* Pattern 2 at candidate's choice: ♩ = 69

PATTERN 1

or PATTERN 2

Printed in Great Britain by Headley Brothers Ltd., The Invicta Press, Ashford, Kent and London.

5/05